Authenticity

Authenticity

Thyrza Eyre

VAKPublishing

Questions regarding the ordering of this book should be addressed to:

VAKPublishing
766 Chenery Street
San Francisco, CA 94131
E-mail: 4authenticity@earthlink.net

http://home.earthlink.net/~4authenticity

Printed in the United States

ISBN 0-9723500-0-4

Cover design and illustration by Alicia Buelow
Typesetting by Charles Miller

ACKNOWLEDGEMENT

Kudos to Mary Menacho for being the messenger who gave spark to the flame.

Keala Hagmann for ensuring that I mind my p's and q's.

Immeasurable gratitude to Charles Miller for his compassion for all creatures in renewal and without whom this book would not exist.

as-salaam alaikum.

Table of Contents

PREFACE

In a world that expects you to fit in, we teach you to stand out.
Working with students in relationships that are respectful and
responsible reflects the essence of the Total Human Development
Model. By first finding their own authentic voice, students can
understand what is important in their world. Then with the support of positive relationships they can move out into the larger
community knowing who they are and what they have to offer.
Our commitment to both the individuality of our students and
their ability to function with a high level of character is the foun-
dation of everything we do.

New Hampton School students are talented artists, athletes,
and leaders. We employ a total human development approach
to teaching and learning which includes the intellectual, emotional and moral as well as the physical and spiritual lives of our
students. NHS adults and young people engage actively and
compassionately in developing their sense of purpose and diverse
talents with the ultimate goal of building a better world. Our
school culture builds an entrepreneurial spirit that emerges natu-
rally from genuine relationships and rigorous learning opportunities. We believe human beings define themselves through their
acts, and we believe intelligence is multifaceted. Therefore, we
strive to link learning to creating and education to experience.
It is for this reason that the Center for Character & Creative
Intelligence at New Hampton School is dedicated to helping students find their individuality within a community and offers this
book as one step in the process.

Jeffrey Pratt Beedy, Ed.D.

INTRODUCTION

INTRODUCTION

…all serious daring starts from within.
– Eudora Welty

You will make an important commitment to yourself by embracing this text as a journey. It's a guide for you to set yourself on your path. If you take it on as homework, or simply devise ways to play the game of 'doing it,' you may fool the instructors and do fine 'in the class.' Don't sell yourself short, it will cost you in more ways than you know. You may believe that the future takes care of itself; there are, however, more than a few 'adult' examples of unhappy people to illustrate it doesn't. The more you discount yourself, the sooner you'll wonder what you've got left. The most important element of life 'to get' is the understanding that there is a core 'You.' This is your authenticity and it is this book's goal to help you maintain it.

Growth presents challenges, painful revelations, and promising insights to your life and potential. In stepping beyond your current self there will be experiences new to you. Some will seem different and others will seriously challenge who you believe yourself to be. You'll find that your thinking will often need to be rethought.

We have all been taught, or absorbed, from our society 'the way things are.' Much of this we have accepted as a lesson mastered due to our desire to learn and our trust of the people we value or once valued. What, however, did we value when we absorbed the beliefs handed down to us? What was the relationship functioning behind these inherited values? Often we hadn't expressed or discovered our own personal values before we took in what was so eagerly given us. We never, especially as children, stopped to think 'it' all out. 'It,' after all, is a large, unending topic with twists, turns, hypocrisy, brutal surprises and nagging doubts – who wants all that, especially when 'it' is told to us, prepackaged, ready made for consumption.

A mind, especially a child's, fresh and unencumbered by 'should haves' (for they'll come later when you look back at the years you're living now), is a sponge sucking up what it can. It's the nature of our acquisitiveness. 'Why? Why? Why?' From age two you did ask the hard questions, persistently. But somewhere after age three that particular persistence slips away, along with its gentle subtext: I'm here, pay attention to me, to what I have to say, to my right to ask whatever I want, when I want, about this new found place in which I live, breathe, exist. Do not blame yourself. Those older than us had often tired of questions long before we posed them. Refresh your curiosity. Don't settle now for what you've been told, not all of it is right for you. You know this already; yet, it's not enough to just know it. It's what you do with that knowledge.

Now you're in your 'teenage years' and make no mistake about it they are among your most important. Certainly there are experiences and responsibilities you have not had yet, but a life without those does not make you a child. You are a young adult and while you may be without all the legal rights and permissions, you are fully an adult. You could be out in the world on your own but are not. The luxury of a wealthy culture is the idea that a young adult can be refined. So great efforts are being made to give you the opportunity to expand your intellectual and creative capacities and knowledge.

In a sense, the economic and social history of your culture (and its value of education and individuality) has created these years between childhood and adulthood. Yet, their naming has not been given much thought. Allow me to suggest they are your fulcrum years: they are meant to leverage you into a future that suits your potential. A fulcrum is also a means by which influence is brought to bear. Therefore, we're working to discover, regain, and secure your authenticity, as it is what you'll work, play and live from throughout your life.

As you begin to engage with your very core, I would like you to give yourself a real sense of exploration. Allow yourself introspection. Some of what you have absorbed and played at being may need to be wrung out. Avoid self-judgment. Be kind to yourself through this process and share that kindness with others. You'll find yourself learning to give room to them to *not* 'be' who you have believed they are.

You will, for your efforts, find yourself in better community as each person fully expresses him or herself in relationship with one another.

T.E.

INFLUENCES

INFLUENCES

Most of the basic material a writer works with
is acquired before the age of fifteen.
– Willa Cather

Take a fresh look at your self. Do not accept pat answers or the routine explanations and phrases you've condensed your child-hood years into. You are looking to see what influences shaped your sense of identity and therefore your life.

We believe our wants and values to be ours so thoroughly that any real search for authenticity must begin by revisiting past experiences, relationships, and events. It is here we discover the roots of our current struggles, successes and expectations. Knowing these roots will help you decide which values are truly your own, which you would like to adopt, and which to discard.

Your goal is to foster a more complete understanding of your-self. How might you evaluate and consider your values and assumptions? What influenced them? What set real or arbitrary limitations? Which of your own values were you given support for?

Favorites
Normally, we do not so much look at things as overlook them.
– Alan Watts

Our favorites can guide us in finding our core. What you find yourself attracted to and seek out are a part of your thinking (intentionally, or otherwise) and will influence your life choices. Important to the growth and fine-tuning of your authenticity is both understanding and appreciating your interests and joys.

Look at your interests and influences more deeply than you may have before. Are they habits, obsessions, or inspirations? Be clear about what they mean to you.

Which artists do you most admire?

Which artistic medium speaks to you most frequently or successfully?

Which writers do you most like to read?

Which magazines do you spend the most time with?

What's your favorite music?

Which lyrics speak strongly to you?

What scientific discovery or application most intrigues you?

What is as yet undiscovered or unsolved that you would truly like to be a part of?

Which leaders (spiritual, political, community, business etc.) inspire you most?

Which one would you most like to meet?

What would you ask him or her?

What sports do you enjoy most?

Which athletes do you admire?

What film's world would you like to live in?

Name three people you might like to be:

For each, list which of their attributes you admire:

Own Values
If everyone is thinking alike, then somebody isn't thinking.
— *Gen. George S. Patton*

Look back in your life to when you first became aware of your own values. Really try to distinguish your own values from those that were taught to you. Remember always that you are working to revitalize your own awareness and sensibility in order to regain your authenticity.

What have you always intuitively known?

Can you say why?

What observations on family and/or society developed the values you have?

What hypocrisy do you see in the world?

What hypocrisy do you allow yourself?

What courage and honesty do you see in the world?

What courage and honesty do you allow yourself?

Experiential Reality

There is no reality except the one contained within us. That is why so many people live such an unreal life. They take the images outside them for reality and never allow the world within to assert itself.
— *Hermann Hesse*

One's literal experiences and emotional responses are what one takes as reality. Each of us absolutely believes in these physical phenomena. You perceive and feel it, and therefore believe it to be real. This reality masquerades as the focal point of your life.

Reality, however, is not a fixed position. Some of what you believe yourself to be is rooted in your past experience. Your current emotions and situations muddy it. Future hopes and anxieties color it. Community joys and dilemmas bracket it. This is all profoundly shaped by particular experience.

Reality, it's suggested, is based upon observation and experience. The question is whose? Human observation and experience is always colored by emotion, culture and prejudice. We hold an opinion of reality based upon insufficient knowledge. No one person's reality is another's. It may be truer to call what we believe to exist around us 'experiential reality' and leave ourselves open to try to unveil what else we might discover of both individual and collective reality.

Reality is either something that we shape and grow into, or it is fixed and predestined. Which do you intuit?

Does reality have capacity or limitation?

Is your life explored or accepted?

Assumptions
I think and think for months and years. Ninety-nine times,
the conclusion is false. The hundredth time I am right.
— Albert Einstein

Examine your assessment of the world. Don't accept everything you've been told. You are working to find your Self in order to develop and freely express your authenticity. Determine what you really believe. Take a hard look at the assumptions you've accepted before you live out false conclusions for the rest of your life.

What do you really believe is unchangeable?

How did you form this belief?

If what you believe is 180 degrees wrong, how would that change the world as you see it?

How would it change your actions and decisions?

Imagining
The man who has no imagination has no wings.
– Muhammad Ali

Another part of your reality is your imagination, for it also reflects your thinking and experience. In fact, it may be the most active part of the thinking from which you function.

What is the nature of your imaginary life?

What values do your imagination keep guard of for you?

What comfort does your imagination give you?

What in your imaginings do you wish existed in your life?

Can you have that for real?

How?

Is there an 'Utopia' to be found in your imaginings?

What ideals or laws for living exist there?

Do you attempt to apply these ideals and laws in your life?

Do they cause you conflict?

Is the conflict fruitful?

Memory

Memory ... everything begins from there. Not only for remembering things but for learning the significance, the place and the time that are inside and behind every word.
– Dario Fo

Memory is how we remember things – not always accurately, but it is what we take from how things were. These impressions shape us. What happened to us or how we were treated shape the point-of-view we have. Memory also holds many of our emotions. A person will always have to face these memories to reconcile them or pay the consequences of attempting to avoid them. I ask you to examine how your memories are currently affecting you.

What, if you could, would you strike from being a part of your past experience?

How does it affect you now?

Is it consuming you?

What is its significance?

Does it effect how you speak about yourself?

What negative words or phrases do you tell yourself?

How do these come out of your past experiences?

How do these words and phrases impact your present?

What are the positive words or phrases you support yourself with?

Authenticity is often revealed in one's positive words and phrases; how is yours?

How frequently do you allow yourself to express your authentic self?

Impact
A life is not important except in the impact it has on other lives.
– Jackie Robinson

Remember the moments when something opened you up and had real impact upon your thinking or life. Consider the breadth of your experience: the personal, the arts, media, sports and recreation, community, events and interactions.

Which moments influenced your thinking?

How were you changed?

What have you read that made you look at your world and life in a different way?

Which experiences most strongly impacted you?

How have your beliefs and influence impacted someone else?

Did this impact reflect what is authentically you?

Journal

I never travel without my diary. One should always
have something sensational to read on the train.
– *Oscar Wilde*

You're on a journey … keep a journal. A journal is an on-going dialogue with one's self and with life. Your thoughts are worth writing, especially for yourself.

A journal is an exercise in thinking. Are you flexing and testing your thoughts? If not, then how will they appear in your life? Thought is an intention of doing something and each day is an opportunity to do it. Your journal can have writings, quotes, photos, drawings, mementos – everything that reflects your own thoughts.

You'll find that many accomplished persons allow themselves a journal: athletes to monitor training, inventors to record ideas, and artists to capture thoughts in process. Da Vinci, who fits both of the last categories, is as well known for his journals as he is for painting *The Last Supper*. Journals are an integral part of one's process. Picasso stated that he painted as a way of keeping a journal. I'd like you to be as prolific in your daily approach to your Self.

CONFINES

CONFINES

And I will return, the phoenix from the flame,
I have learned, I will rise
And you'll see me return, Bein' what I am
– Sinead O'Connor

The mores of your society and the values of your parents will seep into you. As they do, you are at work building your beliefs and defining your own ideals and aspirations. These, which you'll believe to be your own, you'll accept and begin to assume a certain reality. This reality of yours, however strongly individual you are, will be grounded in the geography of the culture surrounding you. Think of each of us as bodies of thoughts and convictions walking over a shared landscape, rubbing shoulders with one another. We experience the beliefs and ideas of others and some of them rub off. There is an irony here then; we gain much of our thoughts and beliefs from others and yet define our very self by what we have taken. Our thinking confines us.

In affirming your passions and reclaiming the core of your Self, you will find a very active need to discard the assumptions and expectations imposed on you by others. There is an inherent cleansing in shedding what has been artificial to you. Like the phoenix, rise up to what is yours.

Territory
Every man has seen the wall that limits his mind.
– Alfred Victor Vigny

Imagine a physical landscape with a fence that exists around the concept of your self and the experience this self contains. The fence establishes the 'territory' of what you take yourself to be and shapes both your viewpoint and what you allow yourself to experience. Your outlook on life is then set and the 'territory' that has been fenced in seldom resurveyed. You simply accept that this is 'you' and go on from there.

Examine how these fences came to be your perimeter. I'd like you to reflect upon what you've gained by believing them to exist as the definition and boundary of Self. You may want to maintain these fences; let's first make sure that the yard they surround is yours.

Take a hard look at what you've accepted by surveying the territory you've limited yourself to.

Where have you drawn the fence lines of your life?

What do your fences let you do?

What do your fences inhibit you from doing?

What are the adults around you wrong about?

What are they right about?

How can you expand the 'territory' in which you live?

In Whose Eyes
Let us not speak of them, but look, and pass on.
Dante Alighieri

Too often, we are living an attempt to match someone else's vision or to meet another person's expectations. It can be very hard to find yourself in all this white noise. Part of the journey of life is questioning and introspection. The richest and most profound questions are often those that challenge the assumptions you've made (or those that you may feel have been forced upon you). With each assumption, there is the possibility of discovering a truer conclusion.

Work also to understand the reasons for your assumptions and the actual motives existing in your relationships with others. While you may find valid reason to blame, don't get stuck in a loop with it. The point is to grow; this is all about your being able to move forward as the genuine you. Parts of what you'll shed will be easier to let go of than others. Remember your motivation and know that the freedom on the other side of this process is waiting for you.

Who am I living for?

Are my choices really for me, or for the dreams and expectations of others?

Does what I spend the most time on give me pleasure?

What do I do for other people, either completely or partially?

What do I get out of doing it for them?

Does it make me happy?

Do the people I do things for pay attention to who I really am?

Are they paying attention to me now?

Am I worthy in their eyes?

Am I worthy in my own?

Limited Self

Each of us has an image of what we think we are or what we should be, and that image, that picture, entirely prevents us from seeing ourselves as we actually are ....
— Jiddu Krishnamurti

You have been living and reacting to all of the events around you with certainty that you know who you are. Even when you are open to reviewing yourself, it is a partial review made by a core self that remains unquestioned. What we believe we are good at or not good at hasn't changed much since second grade. While our mental and physical capabilities have developed greatly since then, the image we hold of ourselves remains the same. We continue to view who we are and 'what we can accomplish' through an old familiar lens.

Despite all of our potential and the unknown opportunities ahead of us, we approach each day with a limited view of self, missing out on much of who we are.

I have thought of myself as:

I've been told I must:

I'll lose my friends if:

If Onlys
I have many regrets, and I'm sure everyone does.
The stupid things you do, you regret ... if you have any sense ...
And if you don't regret them, maybe you're stupid.
– Katharine Hepburn

Resorting to instant (or even distant) replay stems from a desire to change our past. 'If only ...' summons a past before us. It becomes a game of repetition, preventing one from being active in the 'now.' Don't mask today's opportunities by haunting yourself with the past. Instead, find your future by utilizing your command over today.

Let's uproot your 'if onlys' so you can move forward freely.

I would be happier if only in the past:

I would be more of who I am if only I had been born:

I would be loved if only I hadn't:

I would be more successful if only I'd been able to:

'If only ...' takes a stab at the future too. Its trick this time is to misplace the power of your visualizing what you want by obsessing on a false conditional needed for that future. The way one plays this game is to pick a condition you can't meet, anything you're not physically is one destructive start, or select a false condition, say an attribute you'd like to foster but are scared you can't have, or don't believe you can attain (why not sabotage more than one thing at a time?) – and repeat it enough until you actually believe it's true.

Others would understand me better if only:

I would fit in better if only:

I would have more friends if only:

I would be respected if only:

I would be more successful if only:

Once you've got the basic game down, 'if only ...' takes you for double or nothing. It has you so entirely focused on what does not exist, that you forget all of your qualities when it raises the stakes. With sleight of hand 'if only ...' suggests that your ability to succeed at all is in itself conditional on having already succeeded. It's trained you on 'would'. 'I would x if only...' translates to: *X*, that I want in the future, could have been mine now if only I had already done it.

'If only ...' likes playing with you; after all, its twisted logic usually wins. It has no qualms working your uncertainty of your future. While none of us know exactly what's ahead of us, we can stop the 'if only ...' game by putting our energy into envisioning what we want in the future in order to better learn what we're really after.

'Success' is vague; let's determine what you want from it.

What changes do you believe success would bring to your life?

Are these what you want?

Will these satisfy you?

What else do you need?

What else will it take to have what you envision?

Today is what you do have influence over. Don't let 'if only …' convince you that your tomorrows are only a replay of a few moments from your yesterdays. The future is not lived by negating it before it arrives. Oddly enough, despite being preoccupied with it, we don't apply 'if only …' to today.

Try applying the all-knowing 'if only …' in determining what you need now.

I would have the future I want if only today I:

Prison
*I'm not going to limit myself because people won't accept
the fact that I can do something else.*
— *Dolly Parton*

Fill in each cell in the Prison Grid below with a limitation you
believe you have.

	ME	

Assign a separate color to represent each of the following:

Color ◯   Limitations I believe truly to be mine

Color ◯   Limitations I have been burdened with

Color ◯   Limitations I have embraced

Identify each cell in the Prison Grid for the type of limitation it is. Outline the boundary of each of these cells with the color representing its type(s) of limitation.

For each cell in the Prison Grid, define how its limitation has impacted your experience:

Which of the limitations have you accepted as an emotional reality?

Who told you that you had these limitations?

How convinced are you that these are your real limitations?

For each cell, declare what freedom you would gain from escaping its limitation:

What does the idea of these freedoms inspire you to desire?

Which of these desires would you like to fulfill?

TRUTH

TRUTH

*...man will occasionally stumble over the
truth, but usually manages to pick himself up,
walk over or around it, and carry on.*
— *Winston Churchill*

Truth is not meant to be a stumbling block. It is an opportunity,
sometimes painful, other times joyful, to gain realization and
awareness. Truth will put you on a path freer of obstacles than
a path that is not yours. With truth you will find yourself both
at ease and 'in flow,' feeling the sensation of your intellectual,
emotional and physical selves in tune with each other.

You'll move through each day with confidence and mastery.
Soon 'you'll get where you're going', which is determined by
where your honesty with truth is heading you.

While working with your truth and dispelling what works
against your authenticity, further the understanding of your own
thoughts and their value by journaling. Committing sincere
effort to examine your truth and hone your authenticity will
save you from living years, perhaps decades, of false existence
and despair. It is your choice to live resisting truth, or with truth.

See
*Life is like a dogsled team. If you ain't the lead dog,
the scenery never changes.*
— *Lewis Grizzard*

I ask you to see beyond an old view of yourself. Drop the pro-
grammed answers and find the authentic ones. Remove
deceptions and tend to the development of the genuine you.
Authenticity is the one thing you can count on never regretting.

I see myself as:

People see me as:

My family sees me as:

My closest friends see me as:

Of these, which 'me' rules my decision making:

Range
I'd rather be a failure at something I love
than a success at something I hate.
– George Burns

Acknowledge and explore the range of your ability to better understand what is truly yours and how it is meaningful to you.

Of the work and activities you are doing, which do you truly enjoy?

Of the work and activities you are doing, which do you truly care about?

Of what you truly enjoy, what resonates with you?

Of what you truly care about, what resonates with you?

Do you realize that these are passions?

How can you foster these more?

Are you satisfied with your level of engagement with what is meaningful to you?

What brings you a greater sense of being?

Which of your efforts seem fraudulent to you?

Which cause you to feel uncomfortable?

Which do you feel a sense of ease with?

Skills
I believe talent is like electricity.
We don't understand electricity. We use it.
– *Maya Angelou*

Our ability to pursue what we want asks us to develop and build upon our skills. Examine the skills you have and want, and activate them.

What skills do you know you really have?

How are your skills serving you?

What skills would you like to have?

Which skills do you worry you don't have?

Which skills can still be developed?

Which do you want strongly enough to seek help in acquiring them?

Who, or where, might you ask for help?

Are you honest with yourself in your decision of what to spend your energy on?

Could your skills also lead you into new areas of achievement or enjoyment?

Do the skills you have, or are actively working to build, match the future you aspire to?

How do you imagine using your skills in the future?

Fame
Success and failure are equally disastrous.
– Tennessee Williams

Review the people you admire (Favorites in Influences).

What percentage of the people you said you'd like to be are celebrities?

Why might that percentage be what it is?

Do you believe that one needs to be famous to achieve something?

Do you believe that one needs to be famous to be valued by others?

Do you believe that a celebrity is valued any differently by his or her friends after becoming famous?

Do you believe that a celebrity is loved any differently by his or her family after becoming famous?

How do you want to measure your own worth?

Is this how you measure your own worth?

Yearbook

Imagine that there is a yearbook for the first twenty years of life. Would its contents reflect that you were living up to the 'you' you intuit you are?

I'd like written about me:

The people who support me would write:

The phony friends would write:

Who would I most want to have sign this yearbook:

Why?

Who am I too scared to ask to sign this yearbook:

Why?

When were you most surprised by what someone wrote in your school yearbook?

Was it more positive or negative than you expected?

Who disappointed you most by what they wrote in your school yearbook?

What did you learn about your relationship with that person?

What had you hoped to write in someone's yearbook that you didn't get to write?

Would it be positive to share that with them now?

Support
Every time a friend succeeds, I die a little.
– Gore Vidal

Of the people closest to you, are the wrong ones in your support circle and the right ones not invited? We all need help, understanding and encouragement. Have you actively shaped and created a community of support and left the lions at the gate?

List your closest friends:

Now, list positives about each of your closest friends:

List the negatives:

For each friend, note his or her most dominant attribute:

Now turn to asking yourself, 'What do I bring to each of my friends?'

'What do I take?'

'What do I give?'

Are your friends' positive attributes the ones inspiring you?

Are your friends' positive attributes the ones shaping your relationship with them?

Are any of these friendships more negative for you than positive?

Do you want negative relationships?

What are you avoiding in your life?

Are any of your close friends avoiding the same things?

Is there a pattern to your choice of friends?

Which friends handle aspects of life in a way you could learn from?

How have your friends asked you to support them?

Can you and your friends be a community of support for each other?

How do you support their achievement?

How do they support yours?

Dreams
Yet it is in our idleness, in our dreams, that the
submerged truth sometimes comes to the top.
— Virginia Woolf

Dreams I had this week:

A dream I never seem to forget:

Quiet
The quieter you become, the more you can hear.
— Baba Ram Dass

Take the following as a personal experience to have on your own time. It has much to do with the intention of setting out in silence and discovering what comes of it. You may, anticipating that you won't have these full time periods outside of community, choose to create a sign or pin to wear which asks: 'Respect my silence.'

Don't talk for:

4 hours

8 hours

1 day

3 days

5 days

Laughter
He deserves paradise who makes his companions laugh.
– The Qur'an

Humor is one of the ways we view life and reflect our point-of-view. With it, we can reinforce our own outlook or change that of another's. Humor has a great power to reveal.

Is humor incorporated in your outlook?

When is the last time you made someone laugh?

How did it feel?

When is the last time someone made you laugh?

Did it lead you to see a particular situation differently?

How does your humor change in different social situations?

What of yourself does your humor reveal?

Alone
You — you alone have the stars as no one else has them.
— Antoine de Saint-Exupéry

Self is often found while being alone.

My mind wants:

My heart wants:

My soul wants:

I really want to be:

I know I'm to:

Intuition
Often you have to rely on intuition.
— Bill Gates

Our intuition is a guide which is custom made, uniquely our own. Too often it is discounted, as it is not deemed rational. Rational, however, is in the spectrum of group behavior (including the actions of an individual who belongs to a group).

Intuition works purely on an individual level. It's as though we each carry a compass with its own magnetic north.

Intuition demands individual realization and action. Leave your herd mentality for your rational mind. Venture now into honoring and learning to trust and navigate your own course with intuition.

What do you know you have to do?

How long have you known this?

What steps have you taken to answer this call?

What visions of your life do you repeatedly have?

Which would you like to realize?

What excuses do you give yourself for not following your intuition?

If you avoid your intuition will you have the life you want?

Is something else more important than what you want?

Are you tending the importance of what you want?

Does how you live your life reflect your trust of intuition?

Sabotage
We choose our joys and sorrows long before we experience them.
– Kahlil Gibran

We are often the creators of the dilemmas and repetitive behaviors that hold us back. Our creativity would be better spent forming solutions and patterns of action that aid our goals and ideals. Instead, too often, we use this energy against ourselves. Historically, sabotage was something one did to others (I invite you to use a dictionary to explore the meanings of words, for they too have lost much of their authenticity from misuse and neglect).

Examine the patterns shaped by the emotional reactions in your past. Do they serve your 'present?' Will they lead you to the future you realize is yours?

What impediments to success have I put before myself:

Which have I allowed to exist or continue:

How will I conquer these impediments and not accept further compromise:

Do I insist upon setting impossible standards or timeframes to ensure avoiding success or growth?

Do I abandon or neglect what I am good at?

What are the meanest words I say to myself?

What are these words really in reaction to?

The original saboteurs responded to an intolerable situation; what situation provoked your self-sabotage?

An Hour Walk
*It is looking at things for a long time that ripens you
and gives you a deeper understanding.*
— Vincent Van Gogh

Take a walk, alone, for at least forty-five minutes.

What thoughts and intentions came to you?

Were they relevant to your life?

Did they reflect the day you had?

Were they relevant to what you might do to move forward with what's in your life?

How much of the intuition and guidance you found on the walk could you remember without writing it down? Estimate the percentage of your forty-five minute experience that has been lost from your present awareness. What percentage of a lifetime might this grow to be?

TODAY

TODAY

The future is what we are now.
— Jiddu Krishnamurti

Today is the tomorrow you've been waiting for. Tend today, each today. Think actively of how to invest your 'now,' and listen within to discover your future.

You have worked hard to consider the influences, confines, and truth in your life in order to regain and re-establish your authenticity. This work, as in all introspection, pays off in your 'today.' Each morning you wake up to what you've created and fresh opportunity.

Begin to take a look at the infinite that surrounds you. Today is your playground; it's where you begin to find your tomorrows. Have your go at it.

Vision
If the doors of perception were cleansed,
everything would appear to man as it is, infinite.
— William Blake

Examine first how you see. Each of us has a unique perspective; our most valuable, if often underutilized, tool.

What is your take on the world?

What human situation do you have the greatest difficulty in understanding?

What do you not see or understand that a friend does?

What can you see clearly that others fail to see?

What is it you are here to do with your life?

How does that relate to your today?

Can you start to live it now, fully or partially?

Experience
We do not learn by experience,
but by our capacity for experience.
– Buddha

Develop an openness and willingness to experience fully.
Experiencing is not ticking off items on a list. If you live by
only checking off a 'to do list' you may have done many things
at the end of your life but will have experienced very few. Give
yourself quality by expanding your capacity.

What capacity for experience do you have?

What experiences do you resist?

What have you tried repeatedly but are unable to do?

What stops you?

Is it a real or perceived block?

How might you open yourself and avail yourself of that capacity?

Acceptance
A man cannot be comfortable without his own approval.
— Mark Twain

There is a necessity for one to accept one's self. How can you get on with being your self if you are still struggling with whether you care for your self at all?

Three ways I approve of myself:

Destiny
What you can become you are already.
— Friedrich Hebbel

Within you are opportunity and natural inclinations, a knowledge and sensibility of a great potential. I want to encourage you to use it; go after what you're here to do. You may not have acted upon this at all so far, or you may be actively pursuing it. In either case, it is yours to have. It will not go away; it's yours. Seize it so you can live it rather than long for it. Destiny is like a very close friend — long term and a large part of your life. Don't let it be a stranger.

What situation or occupation would allow you to tap the energy of your natural inclinations?

Are you taking advantage of the opportunities being presented to you today?

What is keeping you from your destiny?

Are you honoring your self?

Aim
The purpose of man is in action not thought.
— *Thomas Carlyle*

We don't hit a target without intention. It takes readiness, openness to opportunity, selection, and follow through to get from beginning to end in everything we do. Some targets are bigger than others emotionally. Still others are small, practice targets to build up one's skill at setting intention and completing a process. Keep in mind both your large and small targets as you examine how you take action.

Have you established a clear, focused and defined intent?

Outline the small, manageable steps that make up the path towards what you aim for:

Have you made the steps towards your intention clear and obtainable?

Are you actively taking those steps?

Mentors
Lord we may know what we are,
but know not what we may be.
– William Shakespeare

You're on a path and a map can really help at times, especially when there seems to be a few ways to travel or when you're in for a bumpy ride. Review the people you admire. In your own tastes are the roots of what you yourself want to be. Consider both what appeals to you of their life and the way they became the people you know them to be. Learn from their journey.

Pick the three famous people that you most admire:

Which one would you most like to talk to for two hours?

What do you want to learn from him or her?

What has he or she accomplished that you've not?

Of the three, do any share your adversities?

How did they break from them?

Can you write or meet these people?

What stops you from doing that now?

Pick the three people from your life that you most admire:

Which one has the most to teach you?

What are you expecting he or she could teach?

Have you sought advice from any of these three people?

Do you know how each achieved what they accomplished?

How do you see yourself in them?

Can you seek their guidance now?

What stops you from doing that?

Passion
We could hardly wait to get up in the morning.
– *Wilbur Wright*

Something's got to keep you going and give you the enthusiasm to face each day vigorously. Odds are you'll live a long time; don't let the time you have drain you of the energy that belongs to your passion.

What holds your passion?

Do you hide it from others?

Do you hide it from yourself?

Which topics engage your passion?

What are you excited waking up knowing you get to do?

How many days a week do you get to do this?

Can you have more of what you enjoy in your life?

EPILOGUE

EPILOGUE

There is no end. There is no beginning.
There is only the infinite passion of life.
– Federico Fellini

How the story ends is yours to write. We are each responsible to our own authenticity. It is too intimate and singular for anyone else to know; only you can reveal and live from your core.

Self-discovery and reflection while exciting can also be a painful endeavor. You have come far, bravely, by undertaking the examination this book has asked of you. Some questions, even sections, may remain 'undone.' I expect it. This has not been about filling a book or getting a grade in a class, but finding a way to fulfill your life. I trust that you have developed a better 'in' to your self. I commend you for it. You have faced a great many questions to find the answers you want, within you.

Venture
Life is not a problem to be solved but a reality to be experienced.
– Søren Kierkegaard

I encourage you to build upon the discoveries you have made in the journey of this book. Each time you further reveal and live your authenticity, your capacity for passion is increased. It will fuel your dreams and reveal a new reality for you to experience.

What lies before you has more possibility than you've imagined. Breathe passion into your life; it's everything you've got.

You are your authenticity. Travel well with it.

Fortune
Every individual is the architect of his own fortune.
– Appius Claudius

Design yours.

If you opened a fortune cookie and read the destiny that is truly yours what would it say?

What would your other eleven fortune cookies say?

Author Biography

THYRZA EYRE, born in Honolulu and a graduate of Punahou School, holds a BA and MFA from the UCLA School of Theater, Film and Television.

An award-winning writer-director, Eyre is a member of the Lincoln Center Directors Lab, guest director at the Actors Studio, and former Director-in-Residence of Midnight Shakespeare, a youth discovery theater aiding self-expression through the roles and plays of Shakespeare.

In addition to *Authenticity*, her published works include *Writer's Voice*, a personal exploration for writers into their own creative sources and voice as a writer, *Dialogue From the Outside In*, a study of the structure of dialogue in fiction and drama, and the Film School In A Book™ series on screenwriting, directing, and film and video production. Eyre hosts professional workshops based on her books.